SPANISH-AMERICAN POETRY

A Bilingual Selection

Illustrated by Anne Marie Jauss

HARVEY HOUSE, INC.,
Irvington-on-Hudson, N. Y.

SPANISH-AMERICAN POETRY

A Bilingual Selection

by SEYMOUR RESNICK

Library of Congress Catalog Card No. 64-14514

Manufactured in the United States of America

HARVEY HOUSE, INC.
Publishers
Irvington-on-Hudson, New York

Acknowledgments

The editor and the publishers are grateful for the cooperation of those individual and publishers who granted permission to use their copyrighted material. Ever effort has been made to trace and to acknowledge properly all copyright owner If any acknowledgment has been inadvertently omitted, the publishers will b pleased to make the necessary correction in the next printing.

"The Araucaniad," translated by Charles Maxwell Lancaster and Paul Thoma Manchester. Reprinted with permission of Vanderbilt University Press, Nashvill Tennessee. © 1945 by Vanderbilt University Press from THE ARAUCANIAD

"To Her Portrait," translated by Beatrice Gilman Proske; "Triolet" and "Balla of the Star," translated by Alice Jane McVan. © 1938 by The Hispanic Societ of America. Reprinted by permission of The Hispanic Society of America, Ne York, from TRANSLATIONS FROM HISPANIC POETS.

"On Leaving Cuba," "The Song by the Way," and "Broken Wings," translate by Alice Stone Blackwell. Reprinted with permission of the University of Penn sylvania Press, from SOME SPANISH AMERICAN POETS. © 1929 by Un versity of Pennsylvania Press, Philadelphia, Pa.

"Martin Fierro," translated by Walter Owen. Reprinted with permission of Basi Blackwell & Mott, Limited, Oxford, England. © 1963 by Basil Blackwell & Mot Limited, from THE GAUCHO MARTIN FIERRO.

"When I Die," "The Firewood of St. John," "Solidarity," "Who Knows?" an "Dear Little Man," all translated by Mildred E. Johnson. Reprinted courtesy c the University of Missouri Studies, Columbia, Mo. © 1956 by University of Mi souri Studies, from SWANS, CYGNETS AND OWL.

"Poema 20" by Pablo Neruda. Reprinted with permission of Editorial Losada S.A © 1956 by Editorial Losada S.A. from OBRAS COMPLETAS.

Contents

Preface 7
The Araucaniad TRANSLATED BY C. M. LANCASTER AND P. T. MANCHESTER 10
La Araucana ALONSO DE ERCILLA 11
Foolish Men* 12
Hombres necios SOR JUANA INÉS DE LA CRUZ 13
To Her Portrait TRANSLATED BY BEATRICE GILMAN PROSKE 14
A su retrato SOR JUANA INÉS DE LA CRUZ 15
Privileges of the Poor* 16
Privilegios del pobre JUAN DEL VALLE Y CAVIEDES 17
All My Affection* 18
Todo mi afecto MARIANO MELGAR 19
The Victory of Junin* 20
La victoria de Junín JOSÉ JOAQUÍN OLMEDO 21
Ode to Niagara TRANSLATED BY WILLIAM CULLEN BRYANT 22
Niágara JOSÉ MARÍA HEREDIA 23
On Leaving Cuba TRANSLATED BY ALICE STONE BLACKWELL 24
Al partir GERTRUDIS GÓMEZ DE AVELLANEDA 25
Prayer to God ANONYMOUS 26
Plegaria a Dios PLÁCIDO 27
In the Mouth of the Last Inca TRANSLATED BY ALFRED COESTER 28
En boca del último Inca JOSÉ EUBESIO CARO 29
The Ombu* 30
El ombú LUIS L. DOMÍNGUEZ 31
Martin Fierro TRANSLATED BY WALTER OWEN 32
Martín Fierro JOSÉ HERNÁNDEZ 33
Cry, O Cry, Urutau* 34
Llora, llora, urutaú CARLOS GUIDO Y SPANO 35
Nocturne to Rosario* 36
Nocturno a Rosario MANUEL ACUÑA 37
When I Die TRANSLATED BY MILDRED E. JOHNSON 38
Para entonces MANUEL GUTIÉRREZ NÁJERA 39
Simple Verses* 40
Versos sencillos JOSÉ MARTÍ 41
The Firewood of St. John TRANSLATED BY MILDRED E. JOHNSON 42
Los maderos de San Juan JOSÉ ASUNCIÓN SILVA 43
Nocturne III TRANSLATED BY G. DUNDAS CRAIG 44
Nocturno III JOSÉ ASUNCIÓN SILVA 45
Sonatina* 50
Sonatina RUBÉN DARÍO 51
An Autumn Song in Spring TRANSLATED BY G. DUNDAS CRAIG 52
Canción de otoño en primavera RUBÉN DARÍO 53

Cowardice* 54
Cobardía AMADO NERVO 55
Solidarity TRANSLATED BY MILDRED E. JOHNSON 56
Solidaridad AMADO NERVO 57
If You Are Good* 58
Si eres bueno AMADO NERVO 59
The Song by the Way TRANSLATED BY ALICE STONE BLACKWELL 60
La canción del camino FRANCISCO ICAZA 61
Triolet I TRANSLATED BY ALICE JANE MCVAN 62
Los bienes y las glorias de la vida MANUEL GONZÁLEZ PRADA 63
Triolet II* 64
Algo me dicen tus ojos MANUEL GONZÁLEZ PRADA 65
To Love* 66
Al amor MANUEL GONZÁLEZ PRADA 67
Broken Wings TRANSLATED BY ALICE STONE BLACKWELL 68
Alas rotas FABIO FIALLO 69
Wring the Neck of the Swan TRANSLATED BY G. DUNDAS CRAIG 70
Tuércele el cuello al cisne ENRIQUE GONZÁLEZ MARTÍNEZ 71
The Ballad of Mad Fortune TRANSLATED BY EDNA WORTHLEY UNDERWOOD 72
Balada de la loca fortuna ENRIQUE GONZÁLEZ MARTÍNEZ 73
Who Knows? TRANSLATED BY MILDRED E. JOHNSON 74
¡Quién sabe! JOSÉ SANTOS CHOCANO 75
Song* 78
Tonada LEOPOLDO LUGONES 79
Rocking* 80
Meciendo GABRIELA MISTRAL 81
Night* 82
La noche GABRIELA MISTRAL 83
Ballad of the Star TRANSLATED BY ALICE JANE MCVAN 84
Balada de la estrella GABRIELA MISTRAL 85
Squares and Angles* 86
Cuadrados y ángulos ALFONSINA STORNI 87
Dear Little Man TRANSLATED BY MILDRED E. JOHNSON 88
Hombre pequeñito ALFONSINA STORNI 89
The Hour* 90
La hora JUANA DE IBARBOUROU 91
The Strong Bond* 92
El fuerte lazo JUANA DE IBARBOUROU 93
Poem 20* 94
Poema 20 PABLO NERUDA 95
Index 96

*LITERAL PROSE TRANSLATION BY THE AUTHOR-EDITOR

Preface

Spanish-American Poetry, A Bilingual Selection, has been compiled as a companion volume to the previous *Selections from Spanish Poetry.* It should appeal to the reader with or without a knowledge of Spanish, and may at the same time serve as a useful supplementary text in high school and college classes of Spanish at almost any level. This short collection has several pedagogical aims.

1. Reading and recitation of poetry is an aid in developing good pronunciation. The poems should be read aloud, and many are short enough for easy memorization. Here, one may note that most Spaniards and Spanish-Americans are fond of reciting poetry.

2. Learning of vocabulary and grammatical constructions is facilitated by English translations on facing pages. These translations allow the reader to enjoy the poems without the problem of translating. Twenty selections have literal prose translations, prepared by the editor and arranged to match the corresponding lines of the Spanish original. The others have verse translations, including one by William Cullen Bryant. Although some of these translations do not match the original line for line, there is an aesthetic advantage in having some of the poems represented by poetic equivalents.

3. This volume may serve as a brief introduction to the rich, and often neglected, field ot Spanish-American poetry. The forty selections range from the time of the conquest and colonial period (represented by five poems), through the nineteenth century (fourteen poems) and the first third of the twentieth century

(twenty-one poems). Since a prime consideration in choosing the poems was that they be popular favorites that have endured, the editor has not attempted to include examples of poetry written during the past thirty years. Brief background notes have been provided for each author represented.

For those who prefer to read the selections in order of difficulty rather than in chronological order, the following groupings may serve as a guide:

Simple
The Ombu
Cry, O Cry, Urutau
Simple Verses
Sonatina
An Autumn Song in Spring
Solidarity
The Song by the Way
Triolet I
Triolet II
Broken Wings
Song
Rocking
Squares and Angles
Dear Little Man

Average
Foolish Men
Privileges of the Poor
All My Affection
The Firewood of St. John
Cowardice
If You Are Good
To Love

The Ballad of Mad Fortune
Who Knows?
Night
Ballad of the Star
The Hour
The Strong Bond
Poem 20

Difficult
The Araucaniad
To Her Portrait
The Victory of Junin
Ode to Niagara
In the Mouth of the Last Inca
On Leaving Cuba
Martin Fierro
Prayer to God
Nocturne to Rosario
When I Die
Nocturne III
Wring the Neck of the Swan

The editor hopes that the reader may derive triple pleasure from this volume–from the poems themselves, from the translations and the notes, and from the illustrations that accompany the text.

I wish to thank my friend and colleague, Marion E. Tupper, for many useful suggestions.

S.R.

The Araucaniad

Not of ladies, love, or graces
Do I sing, nor knights enamored,
Nor of gifts and shows of feeling,
Cares of love, or love's affections;
But the valiant acts and prowess
Of those never-daunted Spaniards
Who with swords placed yokes of bondage
On the necks of untamed Indians.

Translated by C. M. Lancaster
and P. T. Manchester

Alonso de Ercilla (1533-1594) was a soldier-poet who took part in the battle against the fierce Araucanian Indians of Chile. His great epic La Araucana *was largely written during lulls in the fighting. We give here the opening stanza.*

La Araucana

No las damas, amor, no gentilezas
de caballeros canto enamorados;
ni las muestras, regalos y ternezas
de amorosos afectos y cuidados;
mas el valor, los hechos, las proezas
de aquellos españoles esforzados,
que a la cerviz de Arauco, no domada,
pusieron duro yugo por la espada.

Alonso de Ercilla

Foolish Men

Foolish men, who do accuse
Women without reason,
Without seeing that you are the cause
Of the very thing you blame.

If with ardor without compare
You woo them when they reject you,
Why do you expect them to behave well
When you incite them to do wrong?

You break down their resistance,
And then gravely
You declare that it was levity on their part
What your persistence achieved.

Translated by S. R.

Sor Juana Inés de la Cruz (1651-1695) was a child prodigy in colonial Mexico. She entered a convent at the age of sixteen, and continued her vast reading and writing until forbidden to do so by her superiors. Her contemporaries called her the "Tenth Muse" because of her great knowledge and beautiful poetry. We give the first three stanzas of her witty poem in defense of women and her famous sonnet on her portrait.

13

Hombres necios

Hombres necios que acusáis
a la mujer sin razón,
sin ver que sois la ocasión
de lo mismo que culpáis:

Si con ansia sin igual
solicitáis su desdén,
¿por qué queréis que obren bien
si las incitáis al mal?

Combatís su resistencia
y luego, con gravedad,
decís que fué liviandad
lo que hizo la diligencia.

Sor Juana Inés de la Cruz

To Her Portrait

14

This trickery of paint which you perceive
With all the finest hues of art enwrought,
Which is false argument of colors taught
By subtle means the senses to deceive—

This by which foolish woman would believe
She could undo the evil years have brought
And conquering in the war against time fought
Could triumph over age, and youth retrieve—

Is all a futile ruse that she has tried,
A fragile flower tossed against the wind,
A useless bribe the power of fate to appease,

A silly effort of mistaken pride,
A base desire, and viewed in rightful mind,
Is dust, a corpse, a shade—is less than these.

Translated by Beatrice Gilman Proske

A su retrato

Este que ves, engaño colorido,
que, del arte ostentando los primores,
con falsos silogismos de colores
es cauteloso engaño del sentido;

Este, en quien la lisonja ha pretendido
excusar de los años los horrores,
y venciendo del tiempo los rigores
triunfar de la vejez y del olvido,

Es un vano artificio del cuidado,
es una flor al viento delicada,
es un resguardo inútil para el hado,

Es una necia diligencia errada,
es un afán caduco y, bien mirado,
es cadáver, es polvo, es sombra, es nada.

Sor Juana Inés de la Cruz

Privileges of the Poor

A poor man is a fool, if he keeps quiet;
If he talks, he is a bore;
If he is intelligent, he is a chatterer;
And if he is affable, he is a hypocrite;
If he is polite, he is a meddler;
When he does not suffer, he is arrogant,
And he is stubborn, when he is determined;
Cowardly, when he is humble;
If he is brave, he is rash;
Presumptuous, if he is discreet;
A flatterer, if he obeys;
And if he excuses himself from doing something, he is rude;
If he has aspirations, he is insolent;
If he is deserving, he is without appreciation;
His nobility is not seen at all,
And his holiday clothing is not neat;
If he works, he is greedy,
And at the other extreme,
He is a vagrant if he rests . . .
Just see what fine privileges these are!

Translated by S. R.

Juan del Valle y Caviedes (1652-1697) was a shopkeeper in colonial Lima who excelled in writing humorous and satirical verse about the society of his day.

17

Privilegios del pobre

El pobre es tonto, si calla;
y si habla es un majadero;
si sabe, es un hablador;
y si afable, es embustero;
si es cortés, entrometido;
cuando no sufre, soberbio;
cobarde, cuando es humilde;
y loco, cuando es resuelto;
si valiente, es temerario;
presumido, si es discreto;
adulador, si obedece;
y si se excusa, grosero;
si pretende, es atrevido;
si merece, es sin aprecio;
su nobleza es nada vista,
y su gala, sin aseo;
si trabaja, es codicioso,
y por el contrario extremo
un perdido si descansa . . .
¡Miren si son privilegios!

Juan del Valle y Caviedes

All My Affection

All my affection I gave to an ungrateful one:
And she was fickle and forgot me.
If in this way one treats
A sincere affection,
Love I do not want,
I do not want to love any more.

We swore that I would be hers and she mine:
I was true, but she did not long remember.
A greater falsehood
I never expect to find,
Love I do not want,
I do not want to love any more.

Her constancy was at one time my glory;
And now her base fickleness causes me to grieve.
It would be shameful
For my attention to continue,
Love I do not want,
I do not want to love any more.

Translated by S. R.

Mariano Melgar (1791-1814) was a brilliant young man—a teacher of mathematics at the university—who joined the revolutionary forces in his native Peru, was captured by the Spaniards and executed at the age of 23. Many of his lyric poems are written in the style of the plaintive love song— yaraví *—of the Aymará and Quechua Indians. We give an example of one of these poems.*

19

Todo mi afecto

Todo mi afecto puse en una ingrata:
y ella inconstante me llegó a olvidar.
Si así, si así se trata
un afecto sincero,
amor, amor no quiero,
no quiero más amar.

Juramos ser yo suyo y ella mía:
yo cumplí, y ella no se acordó más.
Mayor, mayor falsía
jamás hallar espero,
amor, amor no quiero,
no quiero más amar.

Mi gloria fué en un tiempo su firmeza;
y hoy su inconstancia vil me hace penar.
Fuera, fuera bajeza
que durara mi esmero,
amor, amor no quiero,
no quiero más amar.

Mariano Melgar

The Victory of Junin

The horrendous thunder, which bursts with great noise,
Resounding dully, spreads
Through the inflamed sky
And announces the God who reigns in the heavens.

And the flash which in Junín breaks and drives away
The Spanish horde
Which fiercer than ever threatened
With blood and fire eternal slavery:
And the song of victory
Which with a thousand echos spreads, deafening
The deep valley and the craggy peak,
Proclaim Bolívar on earth
Arbiter of peace and war.

Translated by S. R.

José Joaquín Olmedo (1780-1847) of Ecuador celebrated Simón Bolívar's victory over the Spaniards in the decisive battle of Junín with the great classic ode La victoria de Junín. *We give here the first two stanzas of this poem, which contains more than 900 lines. Note the onomatopoetic effect of the rolling* r's *in the opening lines.*

21

La victoria de Junín

El trueno horrendo que en fragor revienta
y sordo retumbando se dilata
por la inflamada esfera,
al Dios anuncia que en el cielo impera.

Y el rayo que en Junín rompe y ahuyenta
la hispana muchedumbre
que más feroz que nunca amenazaba
a sangre y fuego eterna servidumbre:
y el canto de victoria
que en ecos mil discurre ensordeciendo
el hondo valle y enriscada cumbre,
proclaman a Bolívar en la tierra
árbitro de la paz y de la guerra.

José Joaquín Olmedo

Ode to Niagara

My lyre! Give me my lyre! My bosom feels
The glow of inspiration. Oh, how long
Have I been left in darkness, since this light
Last visited my brow! Niagara!
Thou with thy rushing waters dost restore
The heavenly gift that sorrow took away.

Tremendous torrent! For an instant hush
The terrors of thy voice, and cast aside
Those wide-involving shadows, that my eyes
May see the fearful beauty of thy face!
I am not all unworthy of thy sight,
For from my very boyhood have I loved,
Shunning the meaner track of common minds,
To look on Nature in her loftier moods.
At the fierce rushing of the hurricane,
At the near bursting of the thunderbolt,
I have been touched with joy; and when the sea
Lashed by the wind hath rocked my bark, and showed
Its yawning caves beneath me, I have loved
Its danger and the wrath of elements.
But never yet the madness of the sea
Hath moved me as thy grandeur moves me now.

Translated by William Cullen Bryant

José María Heredia (1803-1839) spent most of his short life in exile for anti-Spanish activities in his native Cuba. He often chose as themes for his odes the phenomena of Nature. The ode given here was written when Heredia, then twenty years old, was in exile in the United States.

Niágara

Templad mi lira, dádmela, que siento
en mi alma estremecida y agitada
arder la inspiración. ¡Oh, cuánto tiempo
en tinieblas pasó, sin que mi frente
brillase con su luz . . . ! Niágara undoso,
tu sublime terror sólo podría
tornarme el don divino, que ensañada
me robó del dolor la mano impía.

Torrente prodigioso, calma, calla
tu trueno aterrador: disipa un tanto
las tinieblas que en torno te circundan;
déjame contemplar tu faz serena,
y de entusiasmo ardiente mi alma llena.
Yo digno soy de contemplarte: siempre
lo común y mezquino desdeñando,
ansié por lo terrífico y sublime.
Al despeñarse el huracán furioso,
al retumbar sobre mi frente el rayo,
palpitando gocé: vi al Océano
azotado por austro proceloso
combatir mi bajel, y ante mis plantas
vórtice hirviendo abrir, y amé el peligro.
Mas del mar la fiereza
en mi alma no produjo
la profunda impresión que tu grandeza.

José María Heredia

On Leaving Cuba

Pearl of the sea! Star of the tranquil west!
Beautiful Cuba! Now thy brilliant sky
Night covers with her gloomy veil on high,
As clouds my brow the grief that fills my breast.

I am to leave thee! Toiling without rest,
The crew hoist sail; to aid them, while I sigh,
The breeze of thy warm clime comes eagerly
To tear me from the land I love the best.

Farewell, my native isle, thou Eden dear!
Where'er the wrath of fate my lot may cast,
Thy sweet name ever will delight mine ear.

Farewell! The sail is swelling to the blast;
The anchor lifts; the bark, as if in fear,
Now cleaves the waves, and flies in silence fast!

Translated by ALICE STONE BLACKWELL

Cuba's outstanding poetess, Gertrudis Gómez de Avellaneda (1814-1873), left her beloved island in 1836 to go to Spain with her family. As the ship was sailing from Santiago harbor, she composed the above sonnet.

Al partir

¡Perla del mar! ¡Estrella de Occidente!
¡Hermosa Cuba! Tu brillante cielo
la noche cubre con su opaco velo
como cubre el dolor mi triste frente.

¡Voy a partir! . . . La chusma diligente
para arrancarme del nativo suelo
las velas iza, y pronta a su desvelo
la brisa acude de tu zona ardiente.

¡Adiós, patria feliz, edén querido!
¡Doquier que el hado en su furor me impela,
tu dulce nombre halagará mi oído!

¡Adiós! . . .¡Ya cruje la turgente vela . . .
el ancla alza . . . el buque, estremecido,
las olas corta y silencioso vuela!

Gertrudis Gómez de Avellaneda

Prayer to God

O God of love unbounded! Lord supreme!
In overwhelming grief to Thee I fly.
Rending this veil of hateful calumny,
Oh let Thine arm of might my fame redeem!
Wipe Thou this foul disgrace from off my brow,
With which the world hath sought to stamp it now.

. . . . .

But if this lot Thy love ordains to me,
To yield to foes most cruel and unjust,
To die and leave my poor and senseless dust
The scoff and sport of their weak enmity,
Speak Thou, and then Thy purposes fulfill;
Lord of my life, work Thou Thy perfect will.

ANONYMOUS

Plácido, pseudonym of Gabriel de la Concepción Valdés (1809-1844), a mulatto, was accused of participating in a plot by a group of colored people against the white population of Cuba. He was condemned to death and on his way to execution he recited the moving Plegaria a Dios. *We give the first and last of its six stanzas.*

27

Plegaria a Dios

Ser de inmensa bondad ¡Dios poderoso!
a vos acudo en mi dolor vehemente . . .
¡Extended vuestro brazo omnipotente,
rasgad de la calumnia el velo odioso;
y arrancad este sello ignominioso
con que el hombre manchar quiere mi frente!

. . . . .

Mas si cuadra a tu Suma Omnipotencia
que yo perezca cual malvado impío,
y que los hombres mi cadáver frío
ultrajen con maligna complacencia . . .
suene tu voz, acabe mi existencia . . .
¡Cúmplase en mí tu voluntad, Dios mío!

PLÁCIDO

In the Mouth of the Last Inca

Today arriving on Pichincha's slope,
The deadly cannon of the whites I flee,
Like the sun a wanderer, like the sun aflame,
Like the sun free!

O Sun, my Father, hearken! Manco's throne
Lies in the dust; Thy altar's sanctity
Profaned; exalting Thee alone I pray,
Alone but free!

O Sun, my Father, hearken! A slave before
The nations of the world I'll not agree
To bear the mark. To slay myself I come,
To die though free!

Today Thou wilt perceive me, when afar
Thou dost begin to sink into the sea,
Singing Thy hymns on the volcano's top,
Singing and free!

Tomorrow though, alas! When once again
Thy crown throughout the east will shining be,
Its golden splendor on my tomb will fall,
My tomb though free!

Upon my tomb the condor will descend
From heaven, the condor, bird of liberty,
And building there its nest, will hatch its young,
Unknown and free!

Translated by Alfred Coester

José Eusebio Caro (1817-1853) was a sincere young man, active in Colombian politics. The poem given here extols the strong desire for liberty of many Indian chiefs, to the extreme of choosing death rather than submitting to the Spanish conquerors.

29

En boca del último Inca

Ya de los blancos el cañón huyendo
hoy a la falda del Pichincha vine,
como el sol vago, como el sol ardiendo,
¡como el sol libre!

¡Padre Sol, oye! por el polvo yace
de Manco el trono; profanadas gimen
tus santas aras: yo te ensalzo solo,
¡solo, mas libre!

¡Padre Sol, oye! sobre mí la marca
de los esclavos señalar no quise
a las naciones; a matarme vengo,
¡a morir libre!

Hoy podrás verme desde el mar lejano,
cuando comiences en ocaso a hundirte,
sobre la cima del volcán tus himnos
¡cantando libre!

Mañana sólo, cuando ya de nuevo
por el Oriente tu corona brille,
tu primer rayo dorará mi tumba,
¡mi tumba libre!

Sobre ella el cóndor bajará del cielo;
sobre ella el cóndor que en las cumbres vive
pondrá sus huevos y armará su nido,
¡ignoto y libre!

José Eusebio Caro

The Ombu

30

Each region on earth
Has a prominent feature;
Brazil, its burning sun,
Peru, mines of silver;
Montevideo, its hill;
Buenos Aires—beautiful fatherland—
Has the majestic pampas,
And the pampas have the *ombú.*

Translated by S.R.

Luis L. Domínguez (1819-1898), historian and diplomat, uses the ombú*—a tree typical of the vast Argentine pampas—as the title of his twenty stanza patriotic poem about Argentina. We give here the first stanza, known by heart by almost every Argentine schoolboy.*

El ombú

Cada comarca en la tierra
tiene un rasgo prominente:
el Brasil, su sol ardiente,
minas de plata, el Perú;
Montevideo, su cerro,
Buenos Aires—patria hermosa—
tiene su pampa grandiosa;
la Pampa tiene el Ombú.

LUIS L. DOMÍNGUEZ

Martín Fierro

I sit me here to sing my song
To the beat of my old guitar;
For the man whose life is a bitter cup,
With a song may yet his heart lift up,
As the lonely bird on the leafless tree
That sings 'neath the gloaming star.

May the shining Saints of the heavenly band,
That sing in the heavenly choir,
Come down and help me now to tell
The good and ill that me befell,
And to sing it true to the thrumming strings;
For such is my desire.

. . . . .

And if life fails me, this I know,
When the news of my death is spread,
The roaming gaucho, far away
In the desert lands, will be sad that day,
And a sudden ache in his heart will wake,
When he knows that I am dead.

Translated by WALTER OWEN

In the great epic of Argentine literature, Martín Fierro *(1872), José Hernández (1834-1886) recounts the sad story of a* gaucho*—a cowboy —who was forced to become an outlaw because of the cruel injustice of corrupt officials. So popular was this poem, that a continuation* La vuelta de Martín Fierro *(The Return of Martín Fierro) was published seven years later. We give the first two stanzas, in which the* gaucho *introduces his tale, and one stanza toward the close of the second part of the poem.*

33

Martín Fierro

Aquí me pongo a cantar
al compás de la vihuela,
que el hombre que lo desvela
una pena extraordinaria,
como la ave solitaria
con el cantar se consuela.

Pido a los santos del cielo
que ayuden mi pensamiento:
les pido en este momento
que voy a cantar mi historia
me refresquen la memoria
y aclaren mi entendimiento.

. . . . .

Y si la vida me falta,
ténganlo todos por cierto
que el gaucho, hasta en el desierto,
sentirá en tal ocasión
tristeza en el corazón
al saber que yo estoy muerto.

José Hernández

Cry, O Cry, Urutau

Cry, O cry, urutau
On the branch of the yatay,
No more exists our Paraguay,
Where I was born, and you were, too.
Cry, O cry, urutau.

Translated by S. R.

In 1865 Paraguay's dictator provoked a war with its giant neighbors, Argentina and Brazil. Paraguay was crushed and its male population decimated. The Argentine poet, Carlos Guido y Spano (1827-1918), in the poem Nenia, *records the sad lament of a Paraguayan girl who has lost her family and her sweetheart. In the refrain, which we give here, the* urutaú *is a Paraguayan bird of sweet song and the* yatay *is a type of palm tree. Note the mournful tone skilfully produced by the use of the back vowels* o *and* u *in the opening line.*

35 Llora, llora, urutaú

Llora, llora, urutaú,
en las ramas del yatay;
ya no existe el Paraguay,
donde nací como tú
Llora, llora, urutaú.

CARLOS GUIDO Y SPANO

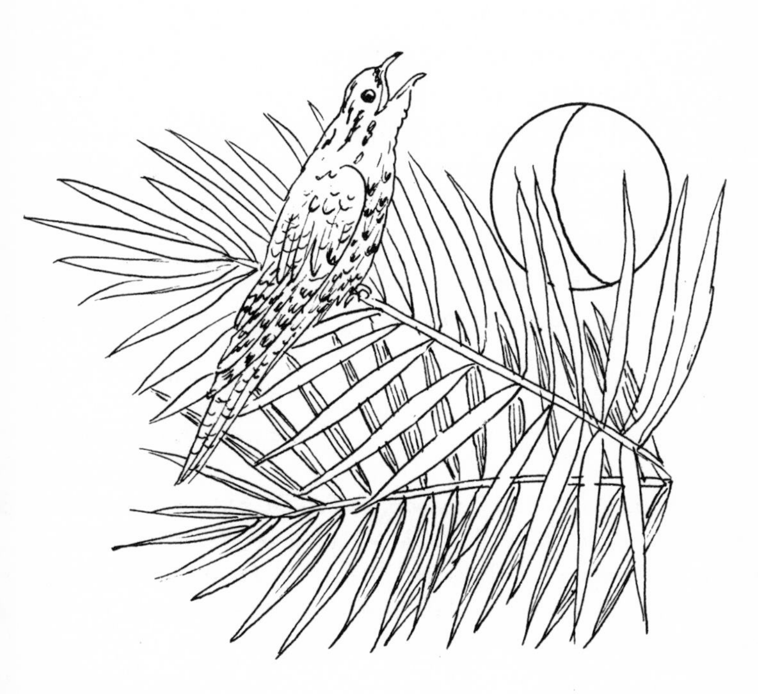

Nocturne to Rosario

Well then! I must
Tell you that I adore you,
Tell you that I love you
With all my heart,
That I suffer much,
That I cry much,
That I can endure it no more,
And crying out I implore you,
I implore you and I speak to you in the name
Of my last illusion.

. . . . .

I understand that your kisses
Will never be mine;
I understand that in your eyes
I shall never see myself;
And I love you, and in my mad
And feverish delirium
I bless your scorn,
I adore your rejection,
And instead of loving you less
I love you even more.

Translated by S. R.

Manuel Acuña (1849-1873), born in Saltillo, Mexico, was a medical student who committed suicide at the age of 24. His Nocturno a Rosario *was written shortly before he took his life and may or may not be related to his suicide. We give the first and fourth of the poem's ten stanzas.*

37

Nocturno a Rosario

¡Pues bien! yo necesito
decirte que te adoro,
decirte que te quiero
con todo el corazón;
que es mucho lo que sufro,
que es mucho lo que lloro,
que ya no puedo tanto,
y al grito en que te imploro
te imploro y te hablo en nombre
de mi última ilusión.

. . . . .

Comprendo que tus besos
jamás han de ser míos,
comprendo que en tus ojos
no me he de ver jamás,
y te amo, y en mis locos
y ardientes desvaríos
bendigo tus desdenes,
adoro tus desvíos,
y en vez de amarte menos,
te quiero mucho más.

Manuel Acuña

When I Die

I wish to die as some fair day is dying,
Upon the sea, my face turned toward the sky,
Where death's dread agony may seem a dream,
My soul, a bird that spreads its wings to fly.

To hear in those last moments that I live,
Accompanied by sky and sea alone,
No prayers nor voices broken by deep sobs,
But only rolling waves' majestic tone.

To die when fading light takes from the waves
Its golden nets and leaves a greenish hue;
To be just like the sun when slowly dying,
A radiance soon vanishing from view.

To die still young, before perfidious time
Destroys the blessed brightness of my days,
While life is still asserting, "I am yours,"
Although we know quite well that she betrays.

Translated by MILDRED E. JOHNSON

Manuel Gutiérrez Nájera (1859-1895) of Mexico is regarded as one of the precursors of modernism in Spanish-American poetry. He wrote excellent short stories as well as poetry. His yearning for an early death, expressed in this poem, was unfortunately realized.

Para entonces

Quiero morir cuando decline el día,
en alta mar y con la cara al cielo;
donde parezca un sueño la agonía,
y el alma, un ave que remonta el vuelo.

No escuchar en los últimos instantes,
ya con el cielo y con la mar a solas,
más voces ni plegarias sollozantes
que el majestuoso tumbo de las olas.

Morir cuando la luz triste retira
sus áureas redes de la onda verde,
y ser como ese sol que lento expira:
algo muy luminoso que se pierde.

Morir, y joven: antes que destruya
el tiempo aleve la gentil corona;
cuando la vida dice aún: "soy tuya,"
¡aunque sepamos bien que nos traiciona!

MANUEL GUTIÉRREZ NÁJERA

Simple Verses

I am a sincere man
From where the palm tree grows,
And before I die I wish
To pour forth the verses from my soul.

. . . . .

I grow a white rose
In July as in January
For the sincere friend
Who gives me his frank hand.

And for the cruel one who tears out
The heart with which I live,
Neither thorn nor thistle do I grow;
I grow the white rose.

Translated by S. R.

José Martí (1853-1895) was the intellectual leader of the Cuban revolution toward the end of the 19th century. His death in 1895, three years before Cuba achieved its independence, was a catastrophe for his country. In addition to being the national hero of Cuba, Martí is one of its finest writers in both prose and verse. We give the opening stanza of his Versos sencillos, *followed by the two stanza poem which Martí is said to have sent to a friend who betrayed him to the Spanish police.*

Versos sencillos

Yo soy un hombre sincero
de donde crece la palma,
y antes de morirme quiero
echar mis versos del alma.

. . . . .

Cultivo una rosa blanca
en julio como en enero,
para el amigo sincero
que me da su mano franca.

Y para el cruel, que me arranca
el corazón con que vivo,
cardo ni ortiga cultivo;
cultivo la rosa blanca.

José Martí

And Asserrín
Aserrán;
Firewood gathered
For St. John
Asks for cheese now,
Bread anon;
That of Roque,
Alfandoque;
That of Rique,
Alfeñique;
That of Trique,
Triquitrán;
Triqui, triqui, triqui, tran!
Triqui, triqui, triqui, tran!

Held by the grandmother on her hard steady knees
The child is swinging back and forth with rhythmic motion,
And both of them are tremulous and agitated,
The grandmother's sweet smile shows motherly devotion,
But something passes through her mind that seems strange fear
For future pains and disillusions to appear,
That her small grandson must endure, whenever fated. . . .

Translated by MILDRED E. JOHNSON

José Asunción Silva (1865-1896) was Colombia's outstanding poet during the early years of modernism (beginning in 1888) and is regarded as one of its most important precursors. Depressed by a series of personal and financial disasters, Silva committed suicide at the age of 31. Los maderos de San Juan, *the first third of which we give, is an elaboration of a nursery rhyme.* Nocturno III, *his masterpiece, was written shortly after the death of his sister.*

43

Los maderos de San Juan

. . . Y aserrín
aserrán,
los maderos
de San Juan
piden queso,
piden pan;
los de Roque,
Alfandoque;
los de Rique,
Alfeñique;
los de Trique,
Triquitrán.
¡Triqui, triqui, triqui, tran!
¡Triqui, triqui, triqui, tran! . . .

Y en las rodillas duras y firmes de la abuela
con movimiento rítmico se balancea el niño,
y entrambos agitados y trémulos están . . .
La abuela se sonríe con maternal cariño,
mas cruza por su espíritu como un temor extraño
por lo que en el futuro, de angustia y desengaño,
los días ignorados del nieto guardarán . . .

José Asunción Silva

Nocturne III

One night,
A night all full of murmurs, of perfumes,
of the music of wings,
A night
In whose nuptial and humid shade burned the
fantastic glowworms,
Slowly by my side, in close embrace, silent and pale,
As if some presentiment of infinite sorrow
Shook to their secret depths the fibers of thy being,
Along the flower-decked path that crossed the plain
Thou walkedst;
And the full moon
Shed over the heavens of deep and boundless blue
its silvery light,
And thy shadow,
Languid and fine,
And my shadow,
Thrown by the moonbeams
Over the dreary sand
Of the path, were joined together,
And were one,
And were one,
And were one long shadow,
And were one long shadow,
And were one long shadow.

45

Nocturno III

Una noche,
una noche toda llena de murmullos, de perfumes
y de músicas de alas;
una noche
en que ardían en la sombra nupcial y húmeda las
luciérnagas fantásticas,
a mi lado lentamente, contra mí ceñida toda, muda y pálida,
como si un presentimiento de amarguras infinitas
hasta el más secreto fondo de las fibras te agitara,
por la senda florecida que atraviesa la llanura
caminabas;
y la luna llena
por los cielos azulosos, infinitos y profundos esparcía
su luz blanca;
y tu sombra
fina y lánguida,
y mi sombra,
por los rayos de la luna proyectadas,
sobre las arenas tristes
de la senda se juntaban;
y eran una,
y eran una,
y eran una sola sombra larga,
y eran una sola sombra larga,
y eran una sola sombra larga.

Tonight
Alone, my soul
Filled with infinite bitterness and agony by thy death,
Parted from thee by time, and distance, and the tomb,
By the black infinitude
Whither no voice of ours can reach,
Silent and alone
Along that path I walked. . .
The sound of dogs was heard baying the moon,
The pallid moon,
And the croak
Of the frogs. . .
I felt a chill. It was the chill that in thy chamber laid its hold
Upon thy cheeks, thy temples, and thy lovely hands,
Amid the snowy whiteness
Of thy winding-sheet.
It was the chill of the tomb, the freezing chill of death,
The chill of nothingness.
And my shadow,
Thrown forward by the moonbeams,
Walked alone,
Walked alone,
Walked alone over the solitary plain;

Esta noche
solo; el alma
llena de las infinitas amarguras y agonías de tu muerte,
separado de ti misma por el tiempo, por la tumba y la distancia,
por el infinito negro
donde nuestra voz no alcanza,
mudo y solo
por la senda caminaba . . .
Y se oían los ladridos de los perros a la luna,
a la luna pálida,
y el chirrido
de las ranas . . .
Sentí frío. Era el frío que tenían en tu alcoba
tus mejillas y tus sienes y tus manos adoradas,
entre las blancuras níveas
de las mortuorias sábanas.
Era el frío del sepulcro, era el hielo de la muerte,
era el frío de la nada.
Y mi sombra,
por los rayos de la luna proyectada,
iba sola,
iba sola,
iba sola por la estepa solitaria;

And thy shadow lithe and nimble,
Languid and fine,
As on that lush, warm night of the spring that's dead,
That night all full of murmurs, of perfumes,
and the music of wings,
Approached and walked with mine,
Approached and walked with mine,
Approached and walked with mine. . . Oh, shades entwined!
Oh, shades of the body that unite with shadows
of the soul!
Oh, shades that seek each other out in the nights of sadness
and tears!

Translated by G. Dundas Craig

y tu sombra esbelta y ágil,
fina y lánguida,
como en esa noche tibia de la muerta primavera,
como en esa noche llena de murmullos, de perfumes
y de músicas de alas,
se acercó y marchó con ella,
se acercó y marchó con ella,
se acercó y marchó con ella . . . ¡ Oh, las sombras enlazadas !
¡ Oh, las sombras de los cuerpos que se juntan con las sombras
de las almas !
¡ Oh, las sombras que se buscan en las noches de tristezas
y de lágrimas !

José Asunción Silva

Sonatina

The princess is sad. . . What can be wrong with the princess?
Sighs escape from her strawberry lips
Which have lost their laughter, which have lost their color.
The princess is pale on her chair of gold,
The sonorous keyboard is silent;
And in a vase there droops a forgotten flower.

Translated by S. R.

Rubén Darío (1867-1916) was born in Nicaragua but lived a great deal in Chile, Argentina and Spain. In 1888, Darío published a volume of prose and poetry entitled Azul *which is taken as the beginning of modernism in Spanish-American poetry. Darío's innovations in language, theme and rhythm had an enormous influence on both sides of the Atlantic, and he is called the "Prince of Modernism." We give the first stanza of his* Sonatina, *and the first three and last three stanzas of* Canción de otoño en primavera. *The latter poem has been called by some critics the finest lyric poem in Spanish since the Golden Age (seventeenth century).*

51

Sonatina

La princesa está triste . . . ¿Qué tendrá la princesa?
Los suspiros se escapan de su boca de fresa,
que ha perdido la risa, que ha perdido el color.
La princesa está pálida en su silla de oro,
está mudo el teclado de su clave sonoro;
y en un vaso olvidada se desmaya una flor.

Rubén Darío

An Autumn Song in Spring

O Youth, divinest of treasures,
No more to return thou art fled;
When I fain would weep, I weep not,
And oft tears unwillingly shed!

A varied tale, though a heavenly,
Has my heart's life-story been.
The first was a sweet maid, joyous,
In a world of grief and teen.

She looked with the pure eyes of dawning,
Her smile had the grace of a flower.
Her tresses had the blackness
Of grief and the midnight hour.

. . . . .

In vain I've sought for the princess
Who was sad with waiting so long.
Life is hard; it embitters, depresses;
There's no princess more for my song.

But in spite of all life's hardness,
My thirst for love has no end;
With my hair turned gray, my footsteps
To the garden of roses I bend.

O Youth, divinest of treasures,
No more to return thou art fled;
When I fain would weep, I weep not,
And oft tears unwillingly shed!

But mine is the Golden Dawn!

Translated by G. Dundas Craig

53 Canción de otoño en primavera

¡Juventud, divino tesoro,
ya te vas para no volver!
¡Cuando quiero llorar, no lloro,
y a veces lloro sin querer! . . .

Plural ha sido la celeste
historia de mi corazón.
Era una dulce niña en este
mundo de duelo y aflicción.

Miraba como el alba pura;
sonreía como una flor.
Era su cabellera oscura
hecha de noche y de dolor.

. . . . .

En vano busqué a la princesa
que estaba triste de esperar.
La vida es dura. Amarga y pesa.
¡Ya no hay princesa que cantar!

Mas a pesar del tiempo terco
mi sed de amor no tiene fin;
con el cabello gris, me acerco
a los rosales del jardín . . .

¡Juventud, divino tesoro,
ya te vas para no volver!
¡Cuando quiero llorar, no lloro,
y a veces lloro sin querer! . . .

¡Mas es mía el Alba de oro!

Rubén Darío

Cowardice

She passed by with her mother. What rare beauty!
What blond hair of light wheat color!
What rhythm in her step! What innate regal
Bearing! What a beautiful figure under the fine tulle!. . .

She passed by with her mother. She turned her head:
She pierced me very deeply with her blue gaze!

I was as in an ecstasy. . . With feverish urgency
Body and soul together cried, "Follow her!"

But I was afraid of loving madly,
Of opening my wounds, which are wont to bleed,
And despite all my thirst for tenderness,
Closing my eyes, I let her pass by!

Translated by S. R.

Amado Nervo of Mexico (1870-1919), a close friend of Darío, was a prolific writer in prose and verse. He had lofty ideals and faith in the innate goodness of man.

Cobardía

Pasó con su madre. ¡Qué rara belleza!
¡Qué rubios cabellos de trigo garzul!
¡Qué ritmo en el paso! ¡Qué innata realeza
de porte! ¡Qué formas bajo el fino tul! . . .

Pasó con su madre. Volvió la cabeza:
¡me clavó muy hondo su mirada azul!

Quedé como en éxtasis . . . Con febril premura
"¡Síguela!" gritaron cuerpo y alma al par.

Pero tuve miedo de amar con locura,
de abrir mis heridas, que suelen sangrar,
¡y no obstante toda mi sed de ternura,
cerrando los ojos, la dejé pasar!

Amado Nervo

Solidarity

56

Little lark, let us sing a song!
Waterfall, let us leap along!
Rivulet, let us run with mirth!
Diamond, let us be very bright!
Eagle, now let us take our flight!
Dawn of day, let us have new birth!
Sing a song!
Leap along!
Run with mirth!
Be very bright!
Take our flight!
Have new birth!

Translated by Mildred E. Johnson

Solidaridad

Alondra, ¡vamos a cantar!
Cascada, ¡vamos a saltar!
Riachuelo, ¡vamos a correr!
Diamante, ¡vamos a brillar!
Águila ¡vamos a volar!
Aurora, ¡vamos a nacer!
¡A cantar!
¡A saltar!
¡A correr!
¡A brillar!
¡A volar!
¡A nacer!

AMADO NERVO

If You Are Good

If you are good, you will know all things
Without books . . . and there will be for your spirit
Nothing illogical, nothing unjust, nothing
Black, in the vastness of the universe.

The unsolvable problem of the ends
And the primary causes,
Which has perplexed philosophy
Will be for you clear and simple.

The world will acquire for your mind
A divine transparency, a clear
Meaning, and your whole being will be enveloped
In an immense peace.

Translated by S. R.

Si eres bueno

Si eres bueno, sabrás todas las cosas,
sin libros . . . y no habrá para tu espíritu
nada ilógico, nada injusto, nada
negro, en la vastedad del universo.

El problema insoluble de los fines
y las causas primeras,
que ha fatigado a la Filosofía,
será para ti diáfano y sencillo.

El mundo adquirirá para tu mente
una divina transparencia, un claro
sentido, y todo tú serás envuelto
en una inmensa paz .

Amado Nervo

The Song by the Way

A solitary pilgrim I,
Through foreign lands I stray;
Yet am I not alone—my song
Goes with me all the way.

And if the night around be black,
I make it bright as day;
I sing, and then the song lights up
The darkness of the way.

I do not sigh for weariness
However far I stray;
The heavenly staff of song makes brief
The distance of the way.

Ah, sad indeed that pilgrim's lot
Who goes alone all day,
Nor has, for comrade of his march,
A song along the way!

Translated by Alice Stone Blackwell

Francisco Icaza (1863-1925), who spent most of his life in Spain as a diplomat, was a distinguished critic as well as one of Mexico's finest poets.

La canción del camino

Aunque voy por tierra extraña
solitario y peregrino,
no voy solo, me acompaña
mi canción en el camino.

Y si la noche está negra,
sus negruras ilumino;
canto, y mi canción alegra
la obscuridad del camino.

La fatiga no me importa
porque el báculo divino
de la canción, hace corta
la distancia del camino.

¡Ay, triste y desventurado
quien va solo y peregrino,
y no marcha acompañado
por la canción del camino!

Francisco Icaza

Triolet I

The pleasures and glories that life can hold
Oh, they come not at all or they come too late.
The flash of their light is sparsely doled,
The pleasures and glories that life can hold.
Pity the man who has grown too old
To pluck the flowers life held in wait.
The pleasures and glories that life can hold
Oh, they come not at all or they come too late.

Translated by ALICE JANE McVAN

Manuel González Prada (1848-1918) was an iconoclast in Peruvian politics and poetry. His poetry is often satirical and witty. González Prada wrote extensively in prose as well as verse.

63

Los bienes y las glorias de la vida

Los bienes y las glorias de la vida
o nunca vienen o nos llegan tarde.
Lucen de cerca, pasan de corrida,
los bienes y las glorias de la vida.
¡Triste del hombre que en la edad florida
coger las flores del vivir aguarde!
Los bienes y las glorias de la vida
o nunca vienen o nos llegan tarde.

MANUEL GONZÁLEZ PRADA

Triolet II

Your eyes are saying something to me;
But what they are saying, I do not know.
Twixt mystery and blushes,
Your eyes are saying something to me.
Are they flashing scorn and anger,
Or do they speak of love and faith?
Your eyes are saying something to me;
But what they are saying, I do not know.

Translated by S. R.

Algo me dicen tus ojos

Algo me dicen tus ojos;
mas lo que dicen no sé.
Entre misterio y sonrojos,
algo me dicen tus ojos.
¿Vibran desdenes y enojos,
o hablan de amor y de fe?
Algo me dicen tus ojos;
mas lo que dicen no sé.

MANUEL GONZÁLEZ PRADA

To Love

If you are a gift snatched from heaven,
Why the doubts, the moans, the tears,
The jealousy, the tormenting grief,
The troubled nights of feverish wakefulness?

If you are an evil from the terrestrial globe,
Why the joys, the happy smiles, the songs,
The hopes, the glorious enchantment,
The visions of peace and consolation?

If you are snow, why your live flames?
If you are a flame, why your inert ice?
If you are a shadow, why do you spread light?

Why the shade, if you are beloved light?
If you are life, why do you give me death?
If you are death, why do you give me life?

Translated by S. R.

67

Al amor

Si eres un bien arrebatado al cielo,
¿por qué las dudas, el gemido, el llanto,
la desconfianza, el torcedor quebranto,
las turbias noches de febril desvelo?

Si eres un mal en el terrestre suelo,
¿por qué los goces, la sonrisa, el canto,
las esperanzas, el glorioso encanto,
las visiones de paz y de consuelo?

Si eres nieve, ¿por qué tus vivas llamas?
si eres llama, ¿por qué tu hielo inerte?
si eres sombra, ¿por qué la luz derramas?

¿Por qué la sombra, si eres luz querida?
si eres vida, ¿por qué me das la muerte?
si eres muerte, ¿por qué me das la vida?

Manuel González Prada

Broken Wings

The prison? It is very sad,
As every place must be
In which, beloved of my soul,
Thou dost not dwell with me.

But if within this prison dark
Thy form should greet mine eyes—
My love, the very thought doth change
My cell to paradise!

Translated by ALICE STONE BLACKWELL

Fabio Fiallo (1866-1942) was a Dominican diplomat, professor and writer. His poetry is often characterized by sentimentality and romanticism.

Alas rotas

¿La cárcel?—Sí; muy triste,
como cualquier recinto
en donde tú, mi amada,
no estés siempre conmigo.

¿Que si a la oscura cárcel
vinieras?—Amor mío,
¡sólo el pensarlo cambia
mi celda en paraíso!

Fabio Fiallo

Wring the Neck of the Swan

Wring the neck of the swan with plumage deceiving,
The note of white upon the lake of blue;
He parades his beauty merely, but has no clue
To the soul of things, no voice in the scene perceiving.

Flee all forms, all language, their harmonies weaving,
That fail to accord with the rhythm deep and true
Of life profound. . . Give adoration due
To life, beyond all risk of misconceiving.

Behold the sapient owl, how he spreads his wings;
From Pallas' lap on Olympus high he springs,
And on yon tree rests from his silent flight. . .

No beauty of the swan has he; but his restless eye,
Which pierces through the darkness, can descry
Deep meanings in the silence of the night.

Translated by G. DUNDAS CRAIG

Enrique González Martínez (1871-1952) was a modernist poet of Mexico who protested against the excesses of modernism, especially an over-ornate style without real substance. His famous sonnet Tuércele el cuello al cisne *(the graceful swan had been chosen by Rubén Darío as the symbol of modernism), written in 1911, signals his revolt against modernism.*

Tuércele el cuello al cisne

Tuércele el cuello al cisne de engañoso plumaje
que da su nota blanca al azul de la fuente;
él pasea su gracia no más, pero no siente
el alma de las cosas ni la voz del paisaje.

Huye de toda forma y de todo lenguaje
que no vayan acordes con el ritmo latente
de la vida profunda . . . y adora intensamente
la vida, y que la vida comprenda tu homenaje.

Mira el sapiente buho cómo tiende las alas
desde el Olimpo, deja el regazo de Palas
y posa en aquel árbol el vuelo taciturno . . .

Él no tiene la gracia del cisne, mas su inquieta
pupila que se clava en la sombra, interpreta
el misterioso libro del silencio nocturno.

Enrique González Martínez

The Ballad of Mad Fortune

With the sun and the sea, the wind and the moon
I'm going to pile up a fortune soon.

With the sun I will mint me coins of gold,
Dark on one side, on the other side bright
To play games of toss-up coin as of old.

I'll bottle the water up out of the sea,
With pretty bright labels, with tags gayly,
I'll sell it with a glass-dropper to keep
For all who want to learn how to weep.

I'll kidnap the wind, then control its flight,
And in nights of quiet with breathlessness blent,
Sell its sighs to lovers for their delight,
And its songs to poets who are silent.

I will keep her a while,
As for the moon,
A kind of protection all of my own,
Safe in my heart's strong-box of stone.

With the sun and the sea, the wind and the moon,
What a mad fortune I'll pile up soon!

Translated by Edna Worthley Underwood

73

Balada de la loca fortuna

Con el sol, el mar, el viento y la luna
voy a amasar una loca fortuna.

Con el sol haré monedas de oro
(al reverso, manchas; al anverso, luz)
para jugarlas a cara o a cruz.

Cerraré en botellas las aguas del mar,
con lindos marbetes y expresivas notas,
y he de venderlas con un cuentagotas
a todo el que quiera llorar.

Robador del viento, domaré sus giros,
y en las noches calladas y quietas,
para los amantes venderé suspiros,
y bellas canciones para los poetas . . .

En cuanto a la luna,
la guardo, por una
sabia precaución,
en la caja fuerte de mi corazón . . .

Con el sol, la luna, el viento y el mar,
¡qué loca fortuna voy a improvisar!

Enrique González Martínez

Who Knows?

"O Indian there at the door
Of your small dwelling, rude and old,
Do you have water for my thirst?
A cover to protect from cold?
A little corn to give me food?
Some place, though poor, for my repose?
Brief quiet for my wanderings?"
"I may have, sir. Who knows?"

"O Indian who wearily
Tills lands that other owners hold,
Do you not know that blood and sweat
Have made them yours from days of old?
Do you not know bold avarice
Took them from you long, long ago?
Do you not know you are the master?"
"It may be, sir. I do not know."

"O Indian with somber brow
And eyes that seem so dull and dead,
What thought does your expression hide
Whose meaning no one ever read?
What are you seeking in your life?
What silent dreams could you disclose?
For what do you beseech your God?"
"Who knows, O sir, who knows?"

¡Quién sabe!

Indio que asomas a la puerta
de esa tu rústica mansión:
¿para mi sed no tienes agua?
¿para mi frío, cobertor?
¿parco maíz para mi hambre?
¿para mi sueño, mal rincón?
¿breve quietud para mi andanza?
—¡Quién sabe, señor!

Indio que labras con fatiga
tierras que de otros dueños son:
¿ignoras tú que deben tuyas
ser, por tu sangre y tu sudor?
¿ignoras tú que audaz codicia,
siglos atrás, te las quitó?
¿ignoras tú que eres el amo?
—¡Quién sabe, señor!

Indio de frente taciturna
y de pupilas sin fulgor:
¿qué pensamiento es el que escondes
en tu enigmática expresión?
¿qué es lo que buscas en tu vida?
¿qué es lo que imploras a tu Dios?
¿qué es lo que sueña tu silencio?
—¡Quién sabe, señor!

Mysterious and ancient race,
Your hearts are wholly fathomless;
You witness joy without delight
And witness pain without distress;
You are august as are the Andes,
The Sun, and the majestic Sea!
That attitude of yours that seems
As if a base servility
Is one of wise indifference
And pride without vindictiveness.

Your blood is running in my veins,
And that same blood exerts such power
If God should ask which I prefer:
The cross or laurel, thorn or flower,
Some sorrow to enrich my song,
Or kisses to assuage my woes,—
In doubt I should respond to him,
"Who knows, O Lord, who knows?"

Translated by MILDRED E. JOHNSON

The Peruvian José Santos Chocano (1875-1924) liked to think of himself as the poet of Spanish America. In his well-known poem ¡Quién sabe! *he identifies with the Indian, whose blood flows in his veins.*

¡Oh raza antigua y misteriosa,
de impenetrable corazón,
que sin gozar ves la alegría
y sin sufrir ves el dolor:
eres augusta como el Ande,
el Grande Océano y el Sol!
Ese tu gesto que parece
como de vil resignación
es de una sabia indiferencia
y de un orgullo sin rencor.

Corre en mis venas sangre tuya,
y, por tal sangre, si mi Dios
me interrogase qué prefiero
—cruz o laurel, espina o flor,
beso que apague mis suspiros
o hiel que colme mi canción—
responderíale dudando:
—¡Quién sabe, señor!

José Santos Chocano

Song

My three dear sisters
Go out to seek a lover.
The eldest says: I want,
I want a king in order to reign.
She became the favorite,
The favorite of the sultan.

The second says: I
Want a true wise man,
Who in youth and beauty
Can immortalize me.
That one married the magician
Of the isle of glass.

The youngest one says nothing,
She can do nothing but sigh.
Of the three sisters she
Is the only one who knows how to love.
She seeks only love,
And she cannot find it.

Translated by S. R.

Leopoldo Lugones (1874-1938) is perhaps the greatest Argentine poet of the twentieth century. Under the influence of his close friend, Rubén Darío, Lugones was at first a brilliant modernist. His later poetry is extremely varied in both subject matter and verse form. We give here one of his simple, popular poems.

Tonada

Las tres hermanas de mi alma
novio salen a buscar.
La mayor dice: yo quiero,
quiero un rey para reinar.
Esa fué la favorita,
favorita del sultán.

La segunda dice: yo
quiero un sabio de verdad,
que en juventud y hermosura
me sepa inmortalizar.
Esa casó con el mago
de la ínsula de cristal.

La pequeña nada dice,
sólo acierta a suspirar.
Ella es de las tres hermanas
la única que sabe amar.
No busca más que el amor,
y no lo puede encontrar.

Leopoldo Lugones

Rocking

The sea its thousands of waves
Divinely rocks.
Listening to the loving seas
I rock my child.

The wind wandering in the night
Rocks the fields of wheat.
Listening to the loving winds
I rock my child.

God in Heaven His thousands of worlds
Rocks without noise.
Feeling His hand in the dark
I rock my child.

Translated by S. R.

Gabriela Mistral (1889-1957), born Lucila Godoy in Chile, represented her country in many parts of the world, and is probably the best loved poetess of Spanish America. Though she herself never married, many of her poems deal with motherhood. She was awarded the Nobel Prize for Literature in 1945.

Meciendo

El mar sus millares de olas
mece, divino.
Oyendo a los mares amantes,
mezo a mi niño.

El viento errabundo en la noche
mece a los trigos.
Oyendo a los vientos amantes,
mezo a mi niño.

Dios Padre sus miles de mundos
mece sin ruido.
Sintiendo su mano en la sombra,
mezo a mi niño.

Gabriela Mistral

Night

So that you may sleep, my child,
The western sky no longer glows:
There is no other glitter than the dew,
No other whiteness than my face.

So that you may sleep, my child,
The road has become still:
No one murmurs but the river;
Nothing exists but I.

The plain has been enveloped in mist.
The blue violet has closed its petals.
Like a hand there now rests
Over the world a peaceful quiet.

I was not cradling only
My child with my singing:
I was lulling the Earth to sleep
To the rhythm of the cradle swaying.

Translated by S. R.

La noche

Por que duermas, hijo mío,
el ocaso no arde más:
no hay más brillo que el rocío,
más blancura que mi faz.

Por que duermas, hijo mío,
el camino enmudeció:
nadie gime sino el río;
nada existe sino yo.

Se anegó de niebla el llano.
Se encogió el suspiro azul.
Se ha posado como mano
sobre el mundo la quietud.

Yo no sólo fuí meciendo
a mi niño en mi cantar:
a la Tierra iba durmiendo
al vaivén del acunar.

Gabriela Mistral

Ballad of the Star

"Star, I am sad.
Tell me, looking from the sky,
Is there another sad as I?"
"Another yet more sad."

"I am lonely, star,
Tell my soul if there can be
Another one so lone as she."
"Yes," says the star.

"See my tears fast flow.
Tell me if another's cares
Make a cloak of tears she wears."
"Another's faster flow."

"Who is she then? Show her,
She who is so sad and lone,
Tell me, if you know her."

"It is I of whom I tell,
Mingled tears and light I shed,
Together with my mystic spell."

Translated by Alice Jane McVan

Balada de la estrella

— Estrella, estoy triste.
Tú dime si otra
como mi alma viste.
— Hay otra más triste.

— Estoy sola, estrella.
Di a mi alma si existe
otra como ella.
— Sí, dice la estrella.

—Contempla mi llanto.
Dime si otra lleva
de lágrimas manto.
— En otra hay más llanto.

— Di quién es la triste,
di quién es la sola,
si la conociste.

— Soy yo, la que encanto,
soy yo la que tengo
mi luz hecha llanto.

Gabriela Mistral

Squares and Angles

86

Houses in a row, houses in a row,
Houses in a row.
Squares, squares, squares.
Houses in a row.
People already have square souls,
Ideas in a row,
And angles on their backs.
I myself shed a tear yesterday
Which was—good heavens—square.

Translated by S. R.

Alfonsina Storni (1892-1938), Argentina's outstanding poetess often expressed her feminist views in her poetry. Depression and illness drove her to suicide in the sea in 1938.

Cuadrados y ángulos

Casas enfiladas, casas enfiladas,
casas enfiladas.
Cuadrados, cuadrados, cuadrados.
Casas enfiladas.
Las gentes ya tienen el alma cuadrada,
ideas en fila
y ángulo en la espalda.
Yo misma he vertido ayer una lágrima,
Dios mío, cuadrada.

Alfonsina Storni

Dear Little Man

88

O my dear little man, O my dear little man,
Free your canary, as it wants to fly away;
For I am your canary my dear little man,
O let me hop and play.

I went inside your cage, O my dear little man,
O little man, within whose cage I now am penned.
I call you "little," for you do not comprehend me,
Will never comprehend.

Nor am I comprehending you, but in the meantime
Please open that cage door, as I wish liberty;
O my dear little man, I loved you half an hour,
So ask no more from me.

Translated by Mildred E. Johnson

Hombre pequeñito

Hombre pequeñito, hombre pequeñito,
suelta a tu canario que quiere volar . . .
yo soy el canario, hombre pequeñito,
déjame saltar.

Estuve en tu jaula, hombre pequeñito,
hombre pequeñito que jaula me das.
Digo pequeñito porque no me entiendes,
ni me entenderás.

Tampoco te entiendo, pero mientras tanto
ábreme la jaula, que quiero escapar;
hombre pequeñito, te amé media hora,
no me pidas más.

Alfonsina Storni

The Hour

Take me now while it is still early
And I carry fresh dahlias in my hand.

Take me now while still is black
My dark head of hair.

Now while my flesh is fragrant,
And my eyes are clear and my skin is pink.

Now while my light foot wears
The lively sandal of springtime.

Now while laughter rings on my lips
Like a bell that is shaken quickly.

Afterwards . . . ah, I know
That later I shall have nothing of this!

Translated by S. R.

Juana de Ibarbourou (born 1895) of Uruguay has been honored with the title of "Juana de América" for her excellent poetry. Love is the frequent theme of her poems. We give the first half of two of her popular poems.

La hora

Tómame ahora que aún es temprano
y que llevo dalias nuevas en la mano.

Tómame ahora que aún es sombría
esta taciturna cabellera mía.

Ahora que tengo la carne olorosa,
y los ojos limpios y la piel de rosa.

Ahora que calza mi planta ligera
la sandalia viva de la primavera.

Ahora que en mis labios repica la risa
como una campana sacudida aprisa.

Después. . . , ¡ ah, yo sé
que nada de eso más tarde tendré!

Juana de Ibarbourou

The Strong Bond

I grew
For you.
Fell me. My acacia
Begs the *coup de grâce* at your hands.

I bloomed
For you.
Cut me. My lily
When it was born did not know if it was flower or wax.

I flowed
For you.
Drink me. The stream
Envies the clearness of my spring.

I grew wings
For you.
Hunt me. Like a moth,
Filled with impatience I circle your flame.

Translated by S. R.

El fuerte lazo

Crecí
para ti.
Tálame. Mi acacia
implora a tus manos el golpe de gracia.

Florí
para ti.
Córtame. Mi lirio
al nacer dudaba ser flor o ser cirio.

Fluí
para ti.
Bébeme. El cristal
envidia lo claro de mi manantial.

Alas dí
por ti.
Cázame. Falena,
rodeo tu llama de impaciencia llena.

JUANA DE IBARBOUROU

Poem 20

I can write the saddest verses tonight.

I can write, for example: "The night is full of stars,
And they twinkle, blue, in the distance."

The night wind blows in the sky and sings.

I can write the saddest verses tonight.
I loved her, and at times she loved me too.

On nights like this I held her in my arms.
I kissed her so many times under the infinite sky.

She loved me, and at times I loved her too.
How could I not have loved her big, still eyes!

I can write the saddest verses tonight.
To think that I do not have her. To think that I have lost her.

Translated by S. R.

Pablo Neruda (born 1904) of Chile is considered by many critics to be Spanish America's greatest contemporary poet. The majority of his poems deal with themes of social significance. Poem 20, *the first third of which is given here, is from an early collection.*

Poema 20

Puedo escribir los versos más tristes esta noche.

Escribir, por ejemplo: "La noche está estrellada,
y tiritan, azules, los astros, a lo lejos."

El viento de la noche gira en el cielo y canta.

Puedo escribir los versos más tristes esta noche.
Yo la quise, y a veces ella también me quiso.

En las noches como ésta la tuve entre mis brazos.
La besé tantas veces bajo el cielo infinito.

Ella me quiso, a veces yo también la quería.
¡Cómo no haber amado sus grandes ojos fijos!

Puedo escribir los versos más tristes esta noche.
Pensar que no la tengo. Sentir que la he perdido.

Pablo Neruda

Index

Acuña, Manuel, 37
Al amor, 67
Alas rotas, 69
Algo me dicen tus ojos, 65
All My Affection, 18
Al partir, 25
La Araucana, 10, 11
The Araucaniad, 10
A su retrato, 15
An Autumn Song in Spring, 52
Balada de la estrella, 85
Balada de la loca fortuna, 73
The Ballad of Mad Fortune, 72
Ballad of the Star, 84
Los bienes y las glorias de la vida, 63
Blackwell, Alice Stone, 24, 60, 68
Broken Wings, 68
Bryant, William Cullen, 22
La canción del camino, 61
Canción de otoño en primavera, 53
Caro, José Eusebio, 28, 29
Chocano, José Santos, 75
Cobardía, 55
Coester, Alfred, 28
Cowardice, 54
Craig, G. Dundas, 44, 52, 70
Cry, O Cry, Urutau, 34
Cuadrados y ángulos, 87
Darío, Rubén, 51, 53
Dear Little Man, 88
Domínguez, Luis L., 31
En boca del último Inca, 29
Ercilla, Alonso de, 10, 11
Fiallo, Fabio, 69
The Firewood of St. John, 42
Foolish Men, 12
El fuerte lazo, 93
Gómez de Avellaneda, Gertrudis, 24, 25
González Martínez, Enrique, 71, 73
González Prada, Manuel, 63, 65, 67
Guido y Spano, Carlos, 35
Gutiérrez Nájera, Manuel, 39
Heredia, José María, 22, 23
Hernández, José, 33
Hombre pequeñito, 89
Hombres necios, 13
La hora, 91
The Hour, 90
Ibarbourou, Juana de, 90, 91, 93
Icaza, Franciseo, 61
If You Are Good, 58
In the Mouth of the Last Inca, 28
Johnson, Mildred E., 38, 42, 56, 74, 88
Juana Inés de la Cruz, Sor, 12, 13, 15
Lancaster, Charles M., 10
Llora, llora, urutaú, 35
Lugones, Leopoldo, 79
Los maderos de San Juan, 43
Manchester, Paul T., 10
Martí, José, 41
Martin Fierro, 32
Martín Fierro, 33
McVan, Alice Jane, 62, 84
Meciendo, 81
Melgar, Mariano, 18, 19
Mistral, Gabriela, 80, 81, 83, 85
Neruda, Pablo, 95
Nervo, Amado, 55, 57, 59
Niágara, 23
Night, 82
La noche, 83
Nocturne III, 44
Nocturno III, 45
Nocturne to Rosario, 36
Nocturno a Rosario, 37
Ode to Niagara, 22
Olmedo, José Joaquín, 20, 21
El ombú, 31
The Ombu, 30
On Leaving Cuba, 24
Owen, Walter, 32
Para entonces, 39
Plácido, 26, 27
Plegaria a Dios, 26, 27
Poem 20, 94
Poema 20, 95
Prayer to God, 26
Privileges of the Poor, 16
Privilegios del pobre, 17
Proske, Beatrice Gilman, 14
¡Quién sabe! 75
Rocking, 80
Si eres bueno, 59
Silva, José Asunción, 43, 45
Simple Verses, 40
Solidaridad, 57
Solidarity, 56
Sonatina, 50
Sonatina, 51
Song, 78
The Song by the Way, 60
Squares and Angles, 86
Storni, Alfonsina, 87, 89
The Strong Bond, 92
To Her Portrait, 14
To Love, 66
Todo mi afecto, 19
Tonada, 79
Triolet I, 62
Triolet II, 64
Tuércele el cuello al cisne, 71
Underwood, Edna Worthley, 72
Valdés, Gabriel de la Concepción, 26
Valle y Caviedes, Juan del, 16, 17
Versos sencillos, 41
La victoria de Junín, 20, 21
The Victory of Junin, 20
When I Die, 38
Who Knows? 74
Wring the Neck of the Swan, 70